Level 1

Building
VOCABULARY
Foundations

Guided
Practice
Book

Authors

Timothy Rasinski, Nancy Padak, Rick M. Newton, and Evangeline Newton

Teacher Created Materials

Credits

Editors
Jodene Smith, M.A.
Kristy Stark, M.A. Ed.

Assistant Editor
Leslie Huber, M.A.

Editorial Director
Lori Kamola, M.S. Ed.

Editor-in-Chief
Sharon Coan, M.S. Ed.

Editorial Manager
Gisela Lee, M.A.

Creative Director
Lee Aucoin

Cover Design
Neri Garcia

Print Production Manager
Don Tran

Print Production
Robin Erickson

ELL Consultant
Carmen Zuñiga Dunlap, Ph.D.
Associate Dean, College of Education
California State University, Fullerton

Publisher
Rachelle Cracchiolo, M.S. Ed.

To order additional copies of this book or any other Teacher Created Materials products, go to www.tcmpub.com or call 1-800-858-7339.

Teacher Created Materials

5301 Oceanus Drive
Huntington Beach, CA 92649-1030
www.tcmpub.com
ISBN 978-1-4258-0546-3
© 2009 Teacher Created Materials Publishing
Reprinted 2010
Made in China

Table of Contents

Part A:
Let's Read

Poetry Fun

Directions: Read the poem. Circle the *-an* words with a
✏. Then make your own poem by filling in the blanks.

> **Jan and Dan**
>
> Diddle diddle dumpling, Jan and Dan
> Cooked their breakfast in a frying pan.
> Ran to school with their good friend Stan,
> Diddle diddle dumpling, Dan and Jan.

Jan and Dan

Diddle diddle dumpling, Jan and Dan.

Cooked their _____ in a frying pan.

Ran to _____ with their good friend Stan,

Diddle diddle dumpling, Dan and Jan.

Part B:
Let's Play with Words

Writing Words

Directions: Add a letter to *-an* to make the word that names each picture.

f   c   m   p   v

1. _____ an   **2.** _____ an

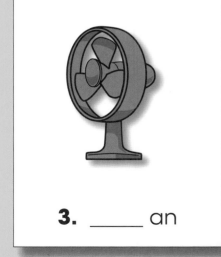

3. _____ an   **4.** _____ an   **5.** _____ an

Part C:
Let's Read

Poetry Fun

Directions: Read the poem. Circle the *-ab* words with a
🖍. Then answer the questions.

Grabby Crabs

King crab, rock crab,
Stone crab, blue crab,
Watch that crab!
It will grab!
Grabby, crabby crabs!

1. How many times is *crab* in the poem? _____

2. How many times is *crabs* in the poem? _____

3. How many times is *crabby* in the poem? _____

Part D:
Let's Play with Words

One and Two

Directions: Name each picture. Use the letters to write each word.

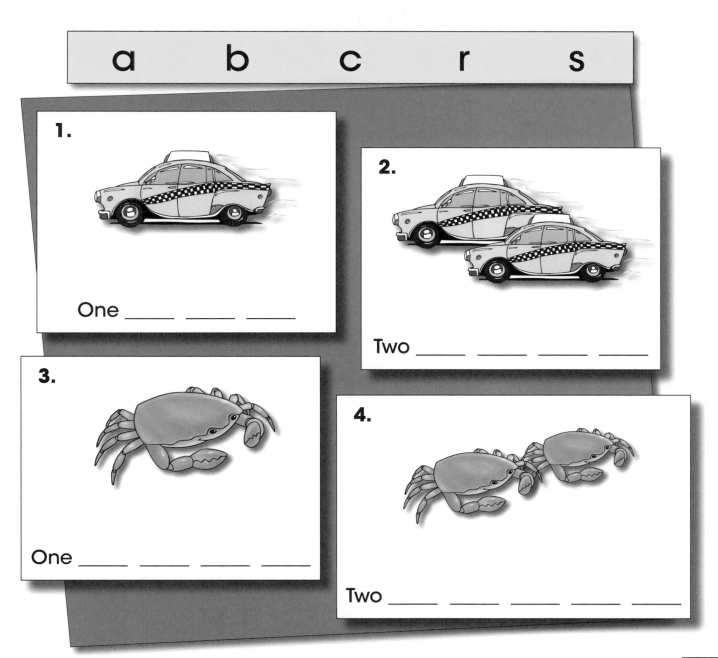

| a | b | c | r | s |

1.

One ____ ____ ____

2.

Two ____ ____ ____ ____

3.

One ____ ____ ____ ____

4.

Two ____ ____ ____ ____ ____

Part E:
Let's Grow

Writing Words

Directions: Name each picture. Write the letters for each word. Circle the *-ab* words with a . Circle the *-an* words with a .

b	c	p	f	l	m	n	a

1.

_____ _____ _____

2.

_____ _____ _____

3.

_____ _____ _____

4.

_____ _____ _____

5.

_____ _____ _____

6.

_____ _____ _____

Poetry Fun

Directions: Read the poems. Circle the *-at* words with a
. Then write three *-at* words from each poem.

Matty Catty
Based on "London Bridge is Falling Down"
Matty Catty sitting flat,
Sitting flat, on the mat.
Matty Catty sitting flat,
My cat, Matty.

-at words

_____

_____

_____

Hattie Potatty
Based on "Humpty Dumpty"
Hattie Potatty sat flat on a mat,
Because Hattie Potatty was just a tad fat.
All the king's horses and all the king's cats
Couldn't put Hattie back on the mat.

-at words _____ _____ _____

Part B:
Let's Play with Words

One and Two

Directions: Name each picture. Use the letters to write each word.

a   b   r   s   t

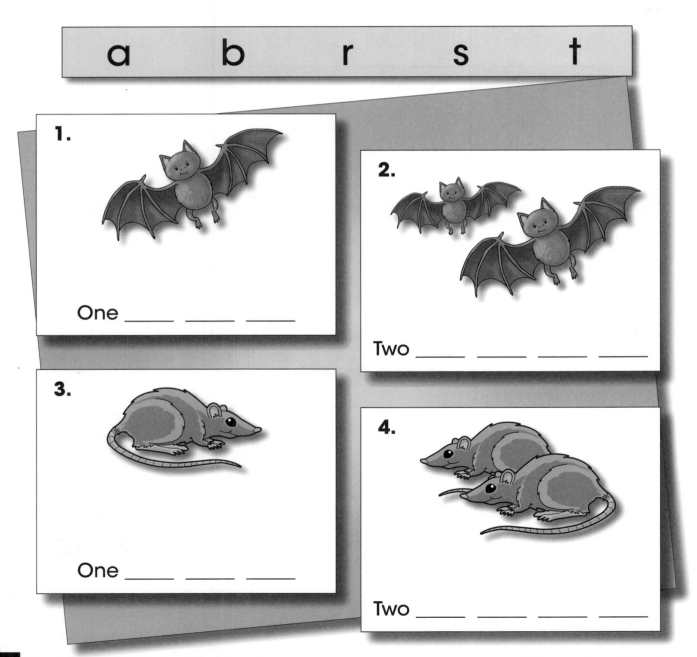

1.

One _____ _____ _____

2.

Two _____ _____ _____ _____

3.

One _____ _____ _____

4.

Two _____ _____ _____ _____

Poetry Fun

Directions: Read the poem. Circle the *-ag* words with a
. Then choose three *-ag* words from the poem and
write them below.

A Rag

Maggie and Aggie picked up a rag,
Waved it like a zigzag flag,
Tugged and pulled and tore a snag,
Then stuffed it in the old rag bag.

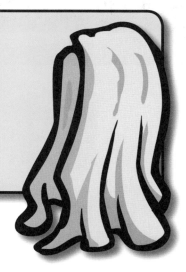

-ag words

_____   _____   _____

Part D:
Let's Play with Words

One and Two

Directions: Name each picture. Use the letters to write each word.

a	b	f	g	l	s

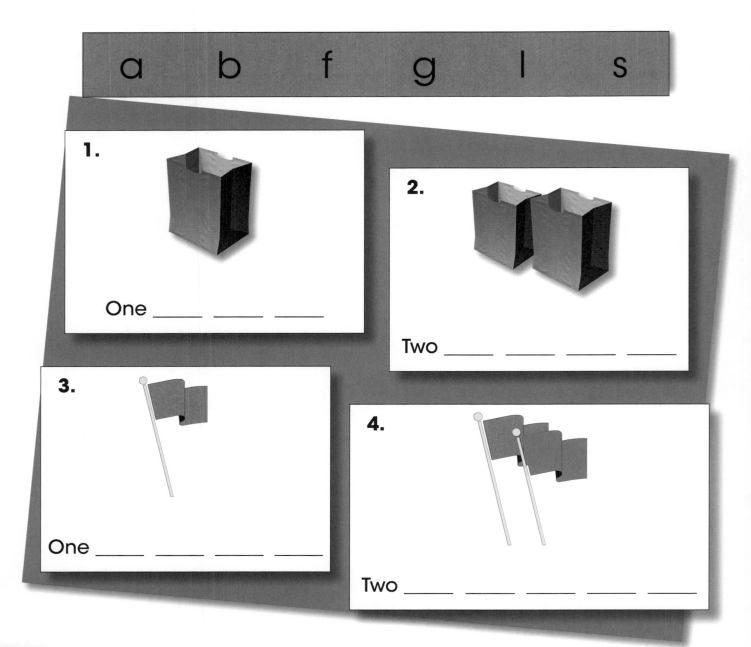

1.

One ____ ____ ____

2.

Two ____ ____ ____ ____

3.

One ____ ____ ____

4.

Two ____ ____ ____ ____

Part E:
Let's Grow

Make Words

Directions: Add the beginning sound to the word family and write the words. Then draw pictures to show the words.

b	-at	-ag
	____ ____ ____	____ ____ ____
r	-at	-ag
	____ ____ ____ ____	____ ____ ____ ____
fl	-at	-ag
	____ ____ ____ ____ ____	____ ____ ____ ____ ____

Part A:
Let's Read

Poetry Fun

Directions: Read the poem. Circle the *-am* words with a
. Then fill in the chart with *-am* words from the poem.

Gram and Pam

Gram, Gram, can I have some jam?
Of course, my darling Pammy.
Bread and jam, bread and jam,
For you and your brother Sammy.

-am at the end	*-am* in the middle

Part B:
Let's Play with Words

Writing Words

Directions: Name each picture. Use the letters to write each word.

a	c	l	m	s

1. 	___ ___ ___ ___
2.	P ___ ___ ___ ___ S ___ ___ ___
3.	___e___ x ___ ___ ___
4.	___c___ ___ ___ ___ ___ ___

Part C:
Let's Read

Poetry Fun

Directions: Read the poem. Circle the *-ad* words with a
. Then fill in the chart with *-ad* words from the poem.

Poor, Poor Tad

Poor, poor Tad was feeling sad.
Poor, poor Chad was feeling mad.
Rain had made the ball field bad;
So they played with mom and dad,
And the lads were finally glad.

One letter before *-ad*	Two letters before *-ad*

Part D:
Let's Play with Words

Writing Words

Directions: Name each picture. Use the letters to write the word.

a   d   g   l   m   p   s

1.  This girl is ____ ____ ____.

2. This boy is ____ ____ ____.

3.  mouse ____ ____ ____

4.  She is ____ ____ ____ ____.

Part E:
Let's Grow

Word Scramble

Directions: Unscramble the letters to make a word. Draw a picture for each word.

1. d d a

___ ___ ___

2. d a s

___ ___ ___

3. a d g l

___ ___ ___ ___

4. a m j

___ ___ ___

5. a m d

___ ___ ___

Part A:
Let's Read

Poetry Fun

Directions: Read the poem. Circle the *-ack* words with a
. Then fill in the chart with *-ack* words from the poem.

Jack and Jill

Jack and Jill went up the stack
To track a little bunny.
Jack fell back,
Upon a crack,
And now he's feeling funny.

One letter before *-ack*	Two letters before *-ack*

Part B:
Let's Play with Words

One and More

Directions: Name each picture. Use the letters to write each word.

a   b   c   k   p   s   r

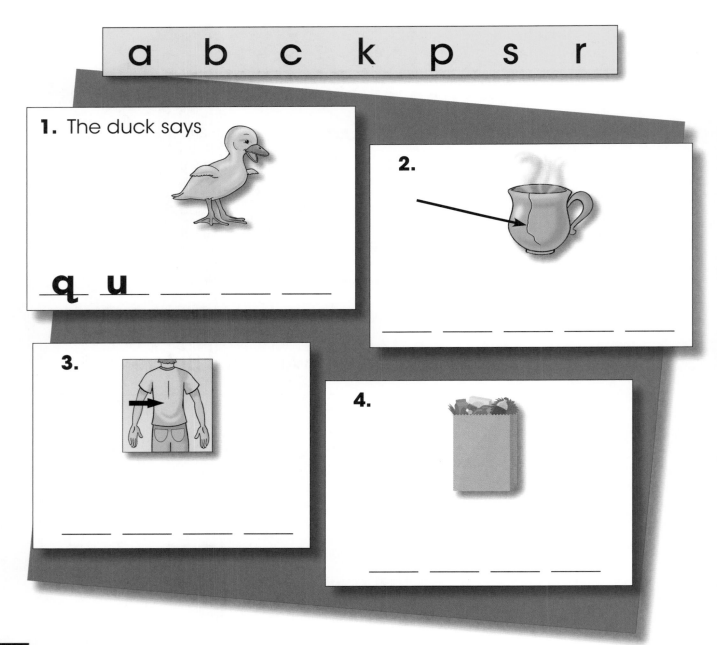

1. The duck says

q u __ __ __ __

2.

__ __ __ __ __ __

3.

__ __ __ __

4.

__ __ __ __ __

Part C:
Let's Read

Poetry Fun

Directions: Read the poem. Circle the *-ap* words with a . Then count the letters in the *-ap* words and write them below.

Flap, Flap, Flap

Flap, flap, flap, hands in the air.
Tap, tap, tap, hands on the chair.
Slap, slap, slap, hands on your lap.
Flap, tap, slap, hands thunderclap!

-ap words with

Three letters   _____

_____

Four letters   _____

_____

Eleven letters   _____

Part D:
Let's Play with Words

Writing Words

Directions: Name each picture. Use the letters to write each word.

| a | l | m | n | p | s |

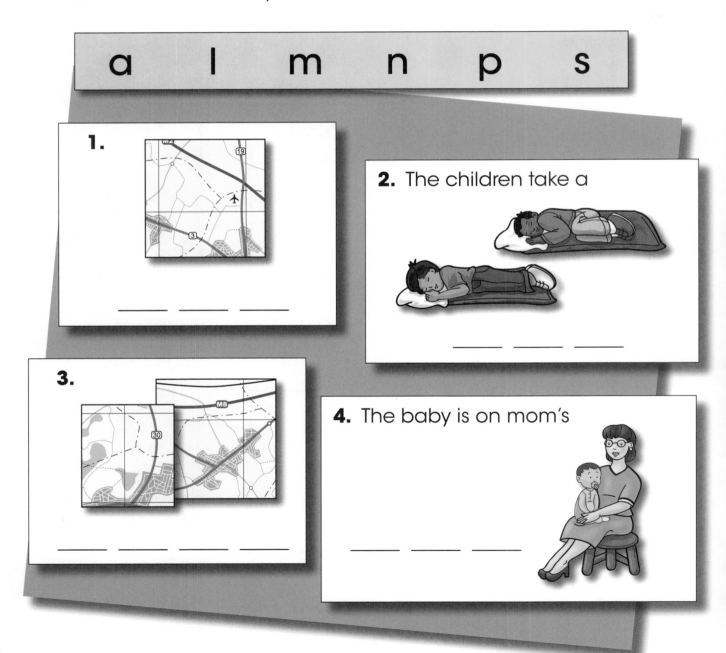

1.

____ ____ ____

2. The children take a

____ ____ ____

3.

____ ____ ____

4. The baby is on mom's

____ ____ ____

Part E:
Let's Grow

Word Scramble

Directions: Name each picture. Use the letters to write the word. Circle the *-ack* words with a ⬛. Circle the *-ap* words with a ⬛.

1.

_____ takes a _____.
      acJk   **anp**

2.

The _____ duck
         abckl

_____ its wings.
      aflps

3.

I ran two _____
                alps

on the _____.
              ackrt

Part A:
Let's Read

Poetry Fun

Directions: Read the poem. Circle the *-in* words with a ✏.
Then count the *-in* words in each line.

Drop the Pin
Based on "Three Blind Mice"

Drop the pin, drop the pin,
Into the bin, into the bin.
I pricked my skin with the point of the pin.
I made such a din and started to spin,
'Til I banged my shin and fell on my chin.
So drop the pin, drop the pin.

---

1. The title has _____ *-in* word.

2. Line 1 has _____ *-in* words.

3. Line 2 has _____ *-in* words.

4. Line 3 has _____ *-in* words.

5. Line 4 has _____ *-in* words.

6. Line 5 has _____ *-in* words.

7. Line 6 has _____ *-in* words.

Part B:
Let's Play with Words

Divide and Conquer

Directions: Divide each word into parts. Then write the word at the end of the row.

| chin | chins | grin | grins |

Word	Beginning	Word Family	Ending	Word
1. chin	_____	_____	**X**	_____
2. chins	_____	_____	_____	_____
3. grin	_____	_____	**X**	_____
4. grins	_____	_____	_____	_____

Part C:
Let's Read

Poetry Fun

Directions: Read the poem. Circle the *-ill* words with a .
Then fill in the chart with *-ill* words from the poem.

A Brand New Pill

Dr. Mill made a brand new pill
That cures you when you're feeling ill.
There is no germ it cannot kill.
All of her patients got a thrill.
But wait 'til they see the doctor's bill!

One letter before *-ill*	More than one letter before *-ill*

word
and
letter
fun

Part D:
Let's Play with Words

Divide and Conquer

Directions: Divide each word into parts. Then write the word at the end of the row.

hill

hills

grill

grills

Word	Beginning	Word Family	Ending	Word
1. hill	_____	_____	**X**	_____
2. hills	_____	_____	_____	_____
3. grill	_____	_____	**X**	_____
4. grills	_____	_____	_____	_____

Part E:
Let's Grow

Word Sort

Directions: Fill in the chart with the words shown below. Write at least one word in each box.

fin

fins

pins

grin

grins

chill

Ends with *-s*	Does not end with *-s*
Has the *-in* word family	**Has the *-ill* word family**

Part A:
Let's Read

Write the Word

Directions: Write the words under the pictures.

1.

_____ _____ _____

2.

_____ _____ _____

3.
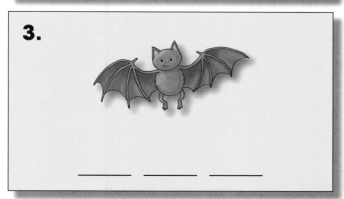
_____ _____ _____

4.

_____ _____ _____

5.
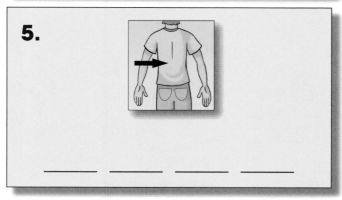
_____ _____ _____

6.
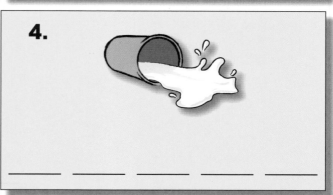
_____ _____ _____

Part B:
Let's Play with Words

Make Sentences

Directions: Choose the correct word to fill in each blank.

1. (pan, plan)   I _____ to buy a new

    _____.

2. (cab, crab)   Have you ever seen a _____

    in a _____?

3. (fat, flat)   With nothing in it, the bag is

    _____. When it is filled, the

    bag is _____.

4. (back, black)   Put the _____ bag in the

    _____ of the car.

5. (spill, spin)   If you _____ the drink,

    it will _____.

Make Words

Directions: Add the beginning sound to the word family. If this makes a real word, write it on the chart.

	-an	-at	-ack
b			
c			

Part D:
Let's Play With Words

Make Words

Directions: Add the beginning sound to the word family. If this makes a real word, write it on the chart.

	-at	**-ack**	**-ap**
s			
t			

Part E:
Let's Grow

Wordo

Directions: This game is like Bingo. Your teacher will give you the words to write in the boxes. Listen to each clue. Use a marker to cover the box for each word you match to the clue. If you get three words in a row, column, or diagonal, call out, "Wordo!"

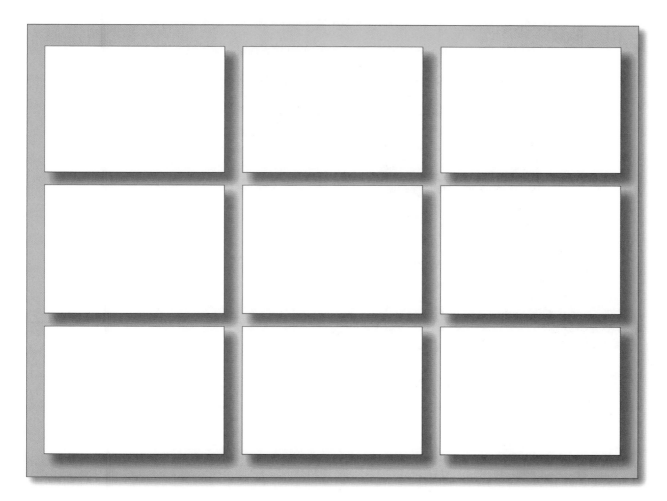

Part A:
Let's Read

Poetry Fun

Directions: Read the poem. Circle the *-it* words. Then write three *-it* words from the poem.

Look at Mit

Lickety split, look at Mit.
How does he get away with it?
With a horse's bit and a doctor's kit,
And talented toes, I must admit.

-it words

_____

_____

_____

Part B:
Let's Play with Words

Divide and Conquer

Directions: Divide each word into parts. Then write the word at the end of the row.

hit   kit   knit   spit

Word	Beginning	Word Family	Word
1. hit	_____	_____	_____
2. kit	_____	_____	_____
3. knit	_____	_____	_____
4. spit	_____	_____	_____

Part C:
Let's Read

Poetry Fun

Directions: Read the poem. Then make a new poem by filling in the blanks with number words. Make sure they add up!

The Emperor's Rings

The Emperor of Ming

Had seven gold rings;

Three from Ching,

Three from Ping,

And one from his wife, Queen Sing.

The Emperor's Ring

The Emperor of Ming

Had _____ golden rings;

_____ from Ching,

_____ from Ping,

And _____ from his wife, Queen Sing.

Part D:
Let's Play with Words

Divide and Conquer

Directions: Divide each word into parts. Then write the word at the end of the row.

　　　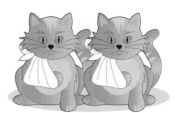

ring　　　rings　　　sling　　　slings

	Word	Beginning	Word Family	Ending	Word
1.	ring	_____	_____	__X__	_____
2.	rings	_____	_____	_____	_____
3.	sling	_____	_____	__X__	_____
4.	slings	_____	_____	_____	_____

Part E:
Let's Grow

Word Sort

Directions: Fill in the chart with the words shown below. Write at least one word in each box.

king

kings

sing

sit

spit

spring

Ends with *-s*	Does not end with *-s*
Has the *-it* word family	**Has the *-ing* word family**

Poetry Fun

Directions: Read the poem. Circle the *-im* words. Then answer the questions.

Tim and Kim

Tim and Kim, both slim and trim,
Decided to swim all day.
The sun got dim, and things looked grim,
So they ran inside to play.

1. Who are the children in the poem?

   _____ and _____

2. What did they want to do? _____

3. Why did they go inside? _____

Part B:
Let's Play with Words

Divide and Conquer

Directions: Divide each word into parts. Then write the word at the end of the row.

Jim

Kim

trim

swim

Word	Beginning	Word Family	Word
1. Jim	_____	_____	_____
2. Kim	_____	_____	_____
3. trim	_____	_____	_____
4. swim	_____	_____	_____

Poetry Fun

Directions: Read the poem. Circle the *-id* words. Then make your own poem by filling in the blanks.

Hey Fiddle Fiddle

Hey fiddle fiddle, "Jump over the middle!"
We called to Sid and to Joe.
So they did; they jumped and slid,
And the kids skidded into the snow.

Hey Fiddle Fiddle

Hey fiddle fiddle, "_____ over the middle!"

We called to _____ and to Joe.

So they did; they _____ and slid,

And the kids skidded into the snow.

Part D:
Let's Play with Words

Divide and Conquer

Directions: Divide each word into parts. Then write the word at the end of the row.

| skid | skids | squid | squids |

	Word	Beginning	Word Family	Ending	Word
1.	skid	_____	_____	**X**	_____
2.	skids	_____	_____	_____	_____
3.	squid	_____	_____	**X**	_____
4.	squids	_____	_____	_____	_____

Part E:
Let's Grow

Word Sort

Directions: Fill in the chart with the words shown below. Write at least one word in each box.

swim   grid   slid   lid

skid   slim   lids

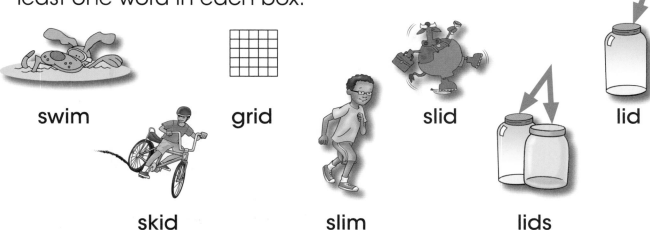

Ends in *-s*	Does not end in *-s*
Has the *-im* word family	Has the *-id* word family
Has one letter before the word family	Has more than one letter before the word family

Part A:
Let's Read

Poetry Fun

Directions: Read the poem. Circle the *-ip* words. Then answer the questions.

Sips and Flips

Can you sip with your lip?
Dunk a chip in some dip?
Do a flip with a skip?
Take a trip on a ship?
Get a grip on a whip?
Then hooray! Hip, hip, hip!

1. How many *-ip* words have three letters? _____

2. How many *-ip* words have four letters? _____

3. How many *-ip* words have five letters? _____

Part B:
Let's Play with Words

word and letter fun

Divide and Conquer

Directions: Divide each word into parts. Write the word at the end of the row. Then use the words to complete the sentences.

clip

clips

skip

trip

Word	Beginning	Word Family	Ending	Word
1. clip	_____	_____	**X**	_____
2. clips	_____	_____	_____	_____
3. skip	_____	_____	**X**	_____
4. trip	_____	_____	**X**	_____

5. I can ____ ____ ____ ____ and hop.

6. Be careful so you don't ____ ____ ____ ____ and fall.

7. Kim has a ____ ____ ____ ____ in her hair.

Part C:
Let's Read

Poetry Fun

Directions: Read the poem. Then make your own poem by filling in the blanks.

Little Carrot Sticks
Based on "Ten Little Indians"

One stick, two sticks, three little carrot sticks,
Four sticks, five sticks, six little pretzel sticks,
Seven sticks, eight sticks, nine little fish sticks,
Ten little sticks to eat!

Little _____ Sticks

One stick, two sticks, three little _____ sticks,

Four sticks, five sticks, six little _____ sticks,

Seven sticks, eight sticks, nine little _____ sticks,

Ten little sticks to eat!

Part D:
Let's Play with Words

Divide and Conquer

Directions: Divide each word into parts. Write the word at the end of the row. Then answer the questions.

lick   Rick   stick   sticks

Word	Beginning	Word Family	Ending	Word
1. lick	_____	_____	**X**	_____
2. Rick	_____	_____	**X**	_____
3. stick	_____	_____	**X**	_____
4. sticks	_____	_____	_____	_____

5. Which one is a boy's name? _____

6. Which one can you do to your lips? _____

7. Which one can you find outside? _____

Part E:
Let's Grow

Word Sort

Directions: Fill in the chart with the words shown below. Write at least one word in each box.

chip

chick

lip

sip

chips

chicks

lick

stick

Ends in *-s*	Does not end in *-s*
Has the *-ip* word family	**Has the *-ick* word family**
Has one letter before word family	**Has more than one letter before word family**

Part A:
Let's Read

Poetry Fun

Directions: Read the poem. Circle the *-ed* words. Then draw a picture of the poem.

Wise Old Ted

Wise Old Ted said to Ed and Fred,
"Both of you just sped to be wed.
Be sure you help to make the bed.
Work hard to keep your families fed.
Take the kids to play on the sled.
Be sure your children are well bred.
And really love your wives," he said.

My Picture

Part B:
Let's Play with Words

Divide and Conquer

Directions: Divide each word into parts. Then write the word at the end of the row.

Word	Beginning	Word Family	Ending	Word
1. sled	_____	_____	**X**	_____
2. sleds	_____	_____	_____	_____
3. shed	_____	_____	**X**	_____
4. sheds	_____	_____	_____	_____

Part C:
Let's Read

Poetry Fun

Directions: Read the poems. Circle the *-ell* words. Then write three *-ell* words from the poems.

Ding Dong Bell

Ding, dong, bell,
A fella's in the well!
Who put him in?
Little Tricia Nell.
Who pulled him out?
Little Ella Stout.

Naughty Nell

What a naughty girl was Nell,
To push a poor fella down the well,
Who never did her any harm,
But kissed her cheek
And praised her charm.

Jingle Bells

Jingle bells, jingle bells,
Riding in the dell.
Oh, how swell to laugh and sing
With those jingle bells!

-ell **words** _____   _____   _____

Part D:
Let's Play with Words

Writing Words

Directions: Name each picture. Use the letters to write each word.

b	e	h	l	l	s	s	y

1.		_____ ell
2.		__ __ __ __
3.		__ __ __ __ __
4.		egg _____ _____ _____ _____ _____
5.		nut _____ _____ _____ _____

Make Words

Directions: Add the beginning sound to the word family. If this makes a real word, write it on the chart.

	-ed	*-ell*
b		
f		
r		
sh		

Part A:
Let's Read

Poetry Fun

Directions: Read the poem. Listen to your partner read the poem to you. Circle the *-est* words. Then write three *-est* words from the poem.

The Old Bird

There lies the empty bird's nest.
This old bird, he's gone out west.
But it's all for the best.
Without his noise, we can rest.

-est words   _____

_____

_____

Part B:
Let's Play with Words

Divide and Conquer

Directions: Divide each word into parts. Then write the word at the end of the row.

Word	Beginning	Word Family	Word
1. quest	_____	_____	_____
2. west	_____	_____	_____
3. chest	_____	_____	_____
4. rest	_____	_____	_____

Part C:
Let's Read

Poetry Fun

Directions: Read the poem. Circle the *-et* words. Then use the words from the Word Bank to write the missing words in the poem below.

Two Cuckoos

Little Bret is starting to fret,
Yvette, his mom, is so upset.
We'll find that old bird, plus one as a pet.
And listen to the chirpy cuckoo duet.

Word Bank: duet   fret   pet   upset

Two Cuckoos

Little Bret is starting to _____ ,

Yvette, his mom, is so _____ .

We'll find that old bird, plus one as a _____ .

And listen to the chirpy cuckoo_____ .

Part D:
Let's Play with Words

Making Compound Words

Directions: Look at each picture. Then put two words together to make a compound word that names each picture.

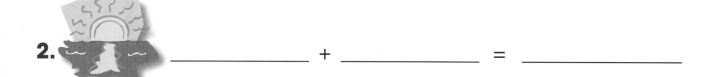

Word Bank: head   room   sun   set   rest

1. _____ + _____ = _____

2. _____ + _____ = _____

3. _____ + _____ = _____

4. _____ + _____ = _____

Part E:
Let's Grow

Word Sort

Directions: Fill in the chart with the words shown below. Write at least one word in each box.

chest   nest   pest

jet   net   pet   vet

Has the *-est* word family	Has the *-et* word family
Has one letter before word family	**Has two letters before word family**

Part A:
Let's Read

Write the Words

Directions: Write the words under the pictures.

1.

_____

2.

__ __ __ __ __

3.

__ __ __

4.

__ __ __ __ __

5.

__ __ __ __

6.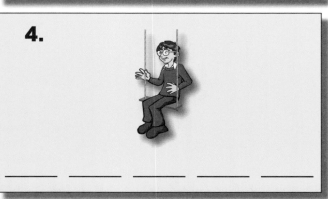

__ __ __ __

Part B:
Let's Play with Words

Make Sentences

Directions: Choose the correct word to fill in each blank.

1. (sick, sing)   I am too _____ to _____ in the

concert.

2. (skin, skip)   Can you _____ with no shoes? Or will

it hurt your _____?

3. (sting, swing)   I got a bee _____ when I was

playing on the _____.

4. (rim, rip)   There is a _____ on the _____

of our basketball net.

5. (trick, trim)   I played a _____ on my dad. I put

feathers on the _____ of his hat.

6. (pet, pest)   My _____ snake is not a

_____.

Make Words

Directions: Add the beginning sound to the word family. If this makes a real word, write it on the chart.

	-in	-ill	-ing
p			
sp			

Part D:
Let's Play with Words

Make Words

Directions: Add the beginning sound to the word family. If this makes a real word, write it on the chart.

	-in	*-ill*	*-et*
gr			
w			

Part E:
Let's Grow

Wordo

Directions: This game is like Bingo. Your teacher will give you the words to write in the boxes. Listen to each clue. Use a marker to cover the box for each word you match to the clue. If you get three words in a row, column, or diagonal, call out, "Wordo!"

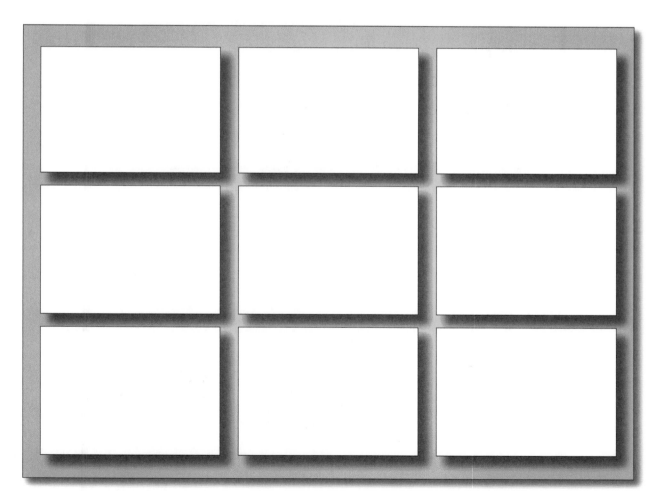

Part A:
Let's Read

Poetry Fun

Directions: Read the poem. Circle the *-ob* words. Then answer the questions.

Jobs and Hobbies

Based on the "Oompa Loompa Song"
from *Charlie and the Chocolate Factory*

Oompa, oba, obity, ooo,
Bob's got a gob of hobbies to do.
Oompa, oba, obity, ooo,
Rob has a job and so does Sue.

1. What is your job? _____

2. What is your hobby? _____

Part B:
Let's Play with Words

Word Sort

Directions: Fill in the chart with words from the Word Bank.

Word Bank: Bob   gob   hobbies   job   Rob

Has three letters	Has more than three letters
Ends with *-ob*	**Does not end with *-ob***

Part C:
Let's Read

Poetry Fun

Directions: Read the poem. Circle the *-ot* words. Then fill in the chart with *-ot* words from the poem.

The Robot

This is the plot
I have not forgot
About Scott Ott,
The chef robot,
Who got a pot
That was hot,
But not too hot
For Scott Ott
The chef robot.

One letter before *-ot*	More than one letter before *-ot*

Part D:
Let's Play with Words

Divide and Conquer

Directions: Divide each word into parts. Then write the word at the end of the row.

Word	Beginning	Word Family	Word
1. plot	_____	_____	_____
2. hot	_____	_____	_____
3. lot	_____	_____	_____
4. not	_____	_____	_____
5. got	_____	_____	_____
6. pot	_____	_____	_____

Part E:
Let's Grow

Make Words

Directions: Add the beginning sound to the word family. If this makes a real word, write it on the chart.

	-ob	-ot
c		
m		
kn		
sl		

Poetry Fun

Directions: Read the poem. Circle the *-op* words. Then fill in the chart with *-op* words from the poem.

The Raindrop

I'm just a little old raindrop,
Hopping down to the bus-stop sign.
I'm just a little old raindrop,
Bopping and slopping in the line.
I'm just a little old raindrop,
Plopping with a flop and a slide.
I'm just a little old raindrop,
Sopping you until you're inside.

-op at end of word	*-op* in the middle of word

Part B:
Let's Play with Words

Make a Poem

Directions: Make a poem by completing the sentences. Use the words from the Word Bank.

Word Bank			
bopping	flop	hopping	raindrop
slopping	stop	sopping	plopping

I'm just a little old _____ ,

_____ on down to the bus-_____ sign.

I'm just a little old _____ ,

_____ and _____ in the line.

I'm just a little old _____ ,

_____ , with a _____ ,

and a slide.

I'm just a little old _____ ,

_____ you until you're inside.

Part C:
Let's Read

Poetry Fun

Directions: Read the poem. Circle the *-ock* words. Write the *-ock* words from the poem and draw a picture of the mouse.

Hickory Mickory Mock

Based on "Hickory Dickory Dock"

Hickory mickory mock,
The mouse watched the clock tick-tock.
Then he ran past,
But not very fast;
Hickory mickory mock.

-ock words	My Picture
_____	
_____	
_____	

Part D:
Let's Play with Words

Divide and Conquer

Directions: Divide each word into parts. Then write the word at the end of the row.

Word	Beginning	Word Family	Ending	Word
1. rocket	_____	_____	_____	_____
2. blocking	_____	_____	_____	_____
3. rocking	_____	_____	_____	_____
4. locket	_____	_____	_____	_____
5. pocket	_____	_____	_____	_____
6. locking	_____	_____	_____	_____

Part E:
Let's Grow

Word Sort

Directions: Fill in the chart with the words shown below. Write at least one word in each box.

hop　　　mop　　　stop　　　rock

sock　　chop　　dock　　drop　　flock

Has one letter before word family	Has two letters before word family
Has the *-op* word family	**Has the *-ock* word family**

Part A:
Let's Read

Poetry Fun

Directions: Read the poem. Circle the *-um* words. Then draw a picture of the poem.

Rub-a-Tum-Tum
Based on "Rub-a-Dub-Dub"

Rub-a-tum-tum,
Three chums in a drum,
And who do you think they be?
A thumpkin, a bumpkin, a summer squash pumpkin;
Dump them all out in the sea.

My Picture

Part B:
Let's Play with Words

Riddle Time

Directions: Write riddles for these words. Then read your riddles to a partner. See if your partner can solve them.

1. drum _____

_____

2. hum _____

_____

Part C:
Let's Read

Poetry Fun

Directions: Read the poem. Circle the *-uck* words. Then fill in the chart with *-uck* words from the poem.

A Mucky Truck

Yuck! What a truck!
It is stuck in the muck,
Oh, what bad luck!
For just a buck,
Mr. Huck
Can wash the muck
Off any truck!

One letter before *-uck*	More than one letter before *-uck*

Part D:
Let's Play with Words

Divide and Conquer

Directions: Divide each word into parts. Then write the word at the end of the row.

Word	Beginning	Word Family	Ending	Word
1. buckle	_____	_____	_____	_____
2. buckling	_____	_____	_____	_____
3. lucky	_____	_____	_____	_____
4. chuckle	_____	_____	_____	_____
5. yucky	_____	_____	_____	_____
6. tucking	_____	_____	_____	_____

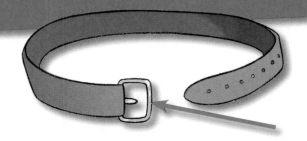

Part E:
Let's Grow

Word Sort

Directions: Fill in the chart with words from the Word Bank. Write at least one word in each box.

Word Bank

bum	chum	mum	strum	drum	plum
buck	puck	Chuck	muck	struck	pluck

Has the *-um* word family	Has the *-uck* word family
Has one letter before word family	**Has more than one letter before word family**

Part A:
Let's Read

Poetry Fun

Directions: Read the poem. Circle the *-ug* words. Draw a picture of the slug. Then write three *-ug* words from the poem.

Ugly Slug
Based on "On Top of Spaghetti"

I walked out this morning, and what did I see?
An ugly slug, Stanley, crawling toward me!
He dug through the green grass, then tugged at my toe.
I slugged that poor slug-bug, without hurting him, though.
He hugged onto my shoelace, and I lugged him to school,
Now ugly slug Stanley learns all the school rules.

My Picture

-ug words

_____

_____

_____

Part B:
Let's Play with Words

Syllable Sort

Directions: Fill in the chart with words from the Word Bank.

Word Bank

bug	drugstore	hug	hugging	mug
plug	slug	tug	tugging	ugly

One syllable (one clap)	Two syllables (two claps)

Part C:
Let's Read

Poetry Fun

Directions: Read the poem. Circle the *-unk* words. Then answer the questions.

Think, Thank, Thunk

Think, thank, thunk,
A test is like a skunk.
You can pass. You can flunk.
But give up, and you're sunk,
'Cause you'll stink, stank, stunk.
So you should think, thank, thunk.

1. Which *-unk* word is an animal? _____

2. Which *-unk* word is in the title of the poem?

_____

Part D:
Let's Play with Words

Syllable Sort

Directions: Fill in the chart with words from the Word Bank.

Word Bank

bunk	chipmunk	clunk	clunky	dunk
dunking	junkyard	junk	skunk	sunk

One syllable (one clap)	Two syllables (two claps)

Part E:
Let's Grow

Make Words

Directions: Add the beginning sound to the word family. If this makes a real word, write it on the chart.

	-ug	-unk
b		
d		
j		
sk		

Part A:
Let's Read

Poetry Fun

Directions: Read the poem. Circle the *-un* words. Draw a picture about the poem. Write a sentence about your picture.

Under the Sun

Under the sun,
We walk or run.
Both can be fun
Under the sun.
When we walk or run,
We're having fun.

My Picture

_____

_____

Part B:
Let's Play with Words

Divide and Conquer

Directions: Write the meaning of the prefix *un-*. Then write what the word means at the end of the row. Finally, use the words to complete the sentences.

Word	Prefix *un-* means	Word means
1. unglue	_____	_____
2. uncooked	_____	_____
3. untie	_____	_____
4. uncross	_____	_____
5. unhappy	_____	_____

6. She is crying. She is _____ .

7. I _____ my shoes to take them off.

8. Raw meat is _____ .

Part C:
Let's Read

Poetry Fun

Directions: Read the poem. Circle the *-ump* words. Fill in the chart with *-ump* words from the poem.

Bossy the Snow Grump
Based on "Frosty the Snowman"

Bossy the Snow Grump
Was a fairy tale they say.
Just a lump of snow,
Yet the children know
How he came to life one day.
Grumpity, thump-thump, thumpity, grump, grump,
Look at Bossy go!
Grumpity, thump-thump, thumpity, grump, grump,
Over the lumps of snow.

Real words	Made-up words

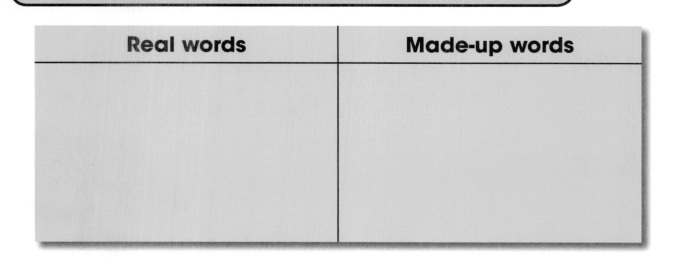

Part D:
Let's Play with Words

Divide and Conquer

Directions: Divide each word into parts. Then write the word at the end of the row.

Word	Beginning	Word Family	Ending	Word
1. thumping	_____	_____	_____	_____
2. grumpy	_____	_____	_____	_____
3. trumpet	_____	_____	_____	_____
4. lumpy	_____	_____	_____	_____
5. dumpster	_____	_____	_____	_____

Part E:
Let's Grow

Wordo

Directions: This game is like Bingo. Your teacher will give you the words to write in the boxes. Listen to each clue. Use a marker to cover the box for each word you match to the clue. If you get three words in a row, column, or diagonal, call out, "Wordo!"

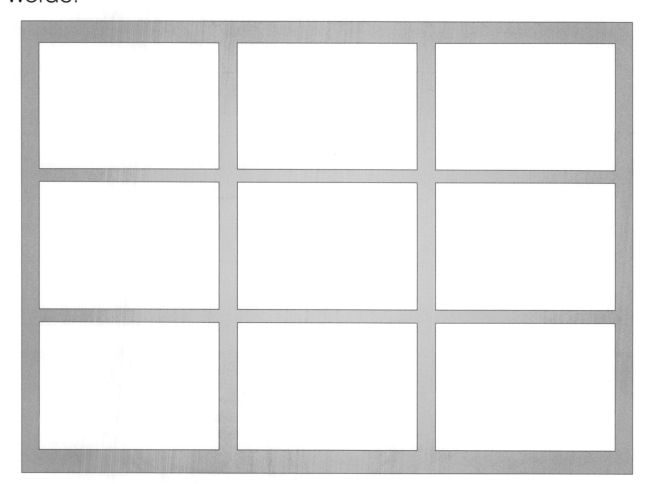

Make Words

Directions: Add the beginning sound to the word family. Fill in the chart with the words you make. For example, *b + -ob = bob*.

b, j, l, ch	-ob
h, sp, f, t	-ot
h, st, t, r	-op
d, r, cl, br	-ock
h, j, tr, t	-unk
sh, j, f, st	-ump

Word	Not a word

Part B:
Let's Play with Words

Make Sentences

Directions: Choose the correct word to fill in each blank. Then draw a picture of one of the sentences. See if your partner can tell what sentence you used.

1. (drop, hot)   I had to _____ the pot. It was too

_____.

2. (clock, job)   At bedtime, my _____ is to check the

_____.

3. (pluck, plum) I will _____ a _____ off the tree.

4. (rug, trunk)   We put our new _____

in the _____ of the car.

• •

My Picture

Make Words

Directions: Add the beginning sound to the word family. If this makes a real word, write it on the chart.

	-ob	-ot	-ug
bl			
sl			

Part D:
Let's Play with Words

Word Sort

Directions: Fill in the chart with words from the Word Bank.

Word Bank					
struck	dug	bum	drum	drug	muck
plum	buck	Chuck	bug	plug	dunk

Has one letter before word family	Has two letters before word family

Rhymes with *gum*	Rhymes with *tuck*	Rhymes with *tug*

Wordo

Directions: This game is like Bingo. Your teacher will give you the words to write in the boxes. Listen to each clue. Use a marker to cover the box for each word you match to the clue. If you get three words in a row, column, or diagonal, call out, "Wordo!"

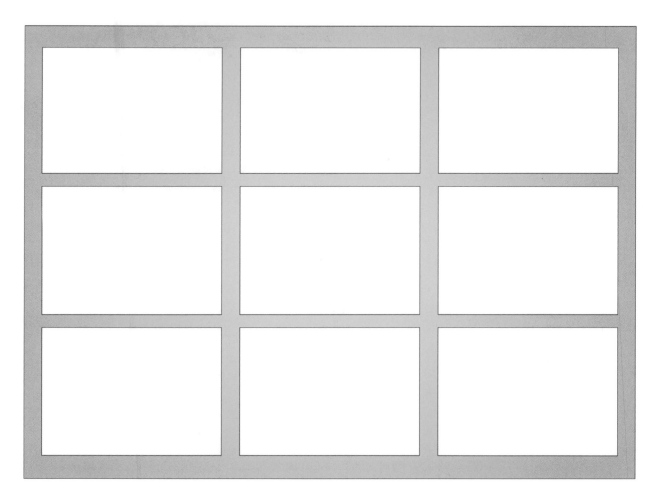

Part A:
Let's Read

Poetry Fun

Directions: Read the poem. Circle the *-ank* words. Then fill in the chart with *-ank* words from the poem.

The Blanket

"Thank you for my blanket,"
Said little Mary Hanket.
"But my brother sank it.
Then my mother shrank it.
Still I love my blanket,"
Said little Mary Hanket.

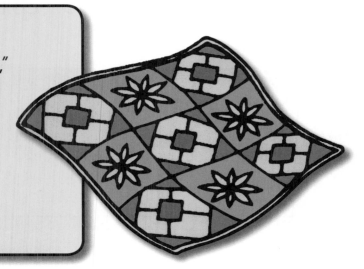

One letter before -ank	Two letters before -ank	Three letters before -ank

Part B:
Let's Play with Words

Riddle Time

Directions: Write riddles for these words. Then read your riddles to a partner. See if your partner can solve them.

1. bank _____

_____

_____

2. thanks _____

_____

_____

Part C:
Let's Read

Poetry Fun

Directions: Read the poem. Circle the *-ink* words. Then fill in the chart with *-ink* words from the poem.

Blink, Wink, Think

Blink, wink, think,
That drink looks like pink ink.
It has a slight stink,
And it could make you shrink.
You should slink to the sink,
Pour it down with a clink,
Blink, wink, think.

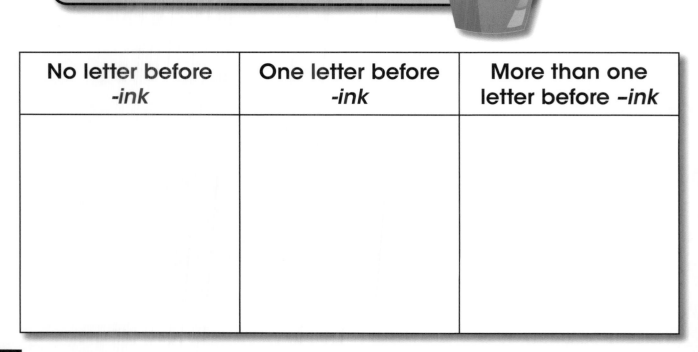

No letter before *-ink*	One letter before *-ink*	More than one letter before *-ink*

Part D:
Let's Play with Words

Divide and Conquer

Directions: Divide each word into parts. Then write the word at the end of the row.

	Word	Beginning	Word Family	Ending	Word
1.	winking	_____	_____	_____	_____
2.	clinks	_____	_____	_____	_____
3.	sprinkle	_____	_____	_____	_____
4.	drinks	_____	_____	_____	_____
5.	twinkle	_____	_____	_____	_____

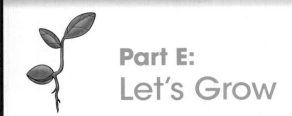

Part E:
Let's Grow

Wordo

Directions: This game is like Bingo. Your teacher will give you the words to write in the boxes. Listen to each clue. Use a marker to cover the box for each word you match to the clue. If you get three words in a row, column, or diagonal, call out, "Wordo!"

Part A:
Let's Read

Poetry Fun

Directions: Read the poem. Circle the *-a__e* words. Then fill in the chart with words from the Word Bank.

Twinkle, Twinkle, Little Flame
Based on "Twinkle, Twinkle, Little Star"

Twinkle, twinkle, little flame,
Barely dancing; who's to blame?
Glaring brightly on our walls,
Burning slowly, down you fall.
Twinkle, twinkle, little flame,
Will you ever be the same?

Word Bank

flame	fade	dancing	what	came
name	late	walls	fall	

Has *-a__e* word family	Does not have *-a__e* word family

Part B:
Let's Play with Words

Divide and Conquer

Directions: Divide each word into parts. Then write the word at the end of the row.

Word	Beginning	Word Family	Word
1. flake	_____	_____	_____
2. scale	_____	_____	_____
3. grade	_____	_____	_____
4. skate	_____	_____	_____
5. plane	_____	_____	_____
6. shame	_____	_____	_____

Poetry Fun

Directions: Read the poem. Circle the *-ain* words. Then answer the questions.

> ### The Rain in Spain
> The rain in Spain stays mainly on the plain.
> The train in Maine obtains passengers in vain.
> The brain in strain leaves teachers in pain,
> But the rain in Spain stays mainly on the plain.

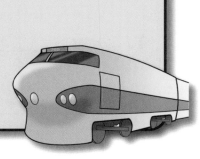

1. How many *-ain* words are in line 1? _____

2. How many *-ain* words are in line 2? _____

3. How many *-ain* words are in line 3? _____

4. How many *-ain* words are in line 4? _____

5. How many different *-ain* words are in the whole poem? _____

Part D:
Let's Play with Words
Riddle Time

Directions: Write riddles for these words. Then read your riddles to a partner. See if your partner can solve them.

1. pain _____

_____

2. drain _____

_____

3. chain _____

_____

Part E:
Let's Grow

Syllable Sort

Directions: Fill in the chart with words from the Word Bank.

Word Bank

erase	complain	shave	behave	unmade
grade	shameful	frame	brain	male
female	locate	crate	plain	raining

One syllable (one clap)	Two syllables (two claps)

Part A:
Let's Read

Poetry Fun

Directions: Read the poem. Circle the -i__e words. Then fill in the chart with words from the Word Bank.

White Mice, White Mice
Based on "Curly Locks"

White mice, white mice,
Will you be mine?
You are very nice,
And you show up on time.
Be sugar and spice
And smile to be seen,
And provide good advice
Like a king or a queen.

Word Bank

white	mice
nice	king
smile	time
advice	will

Has -i__e word family	Does not have -i__e word family

Part B:
Let's Play with Words

Divide and Conquer

Directions: Divide each word into parts. Then write the word at the end of the row.

Word	Beginning	Word Family	Word
1. slice	_____	_____	_____
2. twice	_____	_____	_____
3. shine	_____	_____	_____
4. stride	_____	_____	_____
5. chime	_____	_____	_____
6. strike	_____	_____	_____

Part C:
Let's Read

Poetry Fun

Directions: Read the poem. Circle the *-ight* words. Then fill in the chart with *-ight* words from the poem.

Star Light, Star Bright

Star light, star bright,
First star I see tonight,
I wish I may, I wish I might
Have the wish I wish tonight.

Star bright, star light,
Second star I see this night,
I wish today, I wish tonight
To have a dream that's out of sight!

One syllable (one clap)	Two syllables (two claps)

Part D:
Let's Play with Words

Riddle Time

Directions: Write riddles for these words. Then read your riddles to a partner. See if your partner can solve them.

1. tight _____

_____

2. tonight _____

_____

3. light_____

_____

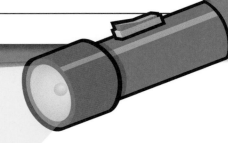

Part E:
Let's Grow

Word Sort

Directions: Fill in the chart with words from the Word Bank.

Word Bank								
ice	mice	might	right	light	tight	hide	ride	lime
time	like	hike	mile	tile	mine	line	live	kite

Has one letter before word family

Has the *-ight* word family

Has the *-i__e* word family

Part A:
Let's Read

Poetry Fun

Directions: Read the poem. Circle the *-ee* words. Then draw a picture to show part of the poem.

Did You Hear That?

Did you hear that?
It sounded like
The eek from an eel,
Or a bee on a tree,
The peal of a beat,
Speeding down the street,
The creak of a wheel,
Or the glee of a spree,
Like a cheep or a peep
From a green mountain sheep!

My Picture

-ee, -ea Word Families

Part B:
Let's Play with Words

Make Words

Directions: Add the beginning sound to the word family. If this makes a real word, write it on the chart.

	-eel	*-eep*
f		
p		
sh		
st		
sw		

Part C:
Let's Read

Poetry Fun

Directions: Read the poem. Circle the *-ea* words. Then fill in the chart with words from the Word Bank.

Take Your Seat

Take your seat.
Heat your meat.
Peel a pea.
Eat whole wheat.
Bare a bean.
Clear and clean.
Take a treat.
Now leave your seat!

Word Bank

heat	meat	seat	pea	bean
eat	wheat	clean	clear	treat

Food	Not food

Part D:
Let's Play with Words

Word Sort

Directions: Fill in the chart with words from the Word Bank.

Word Bank
pea sea bread head sneak speak bear wear pear

Long e	Not long e

Part E:
Let's Grow

Word Sort

Directions: Fill in the chart with words from the Word Bank.

Word Bank

| bee | beat | tee | treat | seed | seat |
| hear | heat | heel | cheer | cheat | week |

Has one letter before word family	Has more than one letter before word family
Has the -ee word family	**Has the -ea word family**

Part A:
Let's Read

Poetry Fun

Directions: Read the poem. Circle the *-o__e* words. Then fill in the chart with *-o__e* words from the poem.

Don't Joke

Please don't hit, and please don't poke.
Hurting others is not a joke.
Sticks and stones can break some bones.
You'll have no friends; you'll be alone.
Be a good friend; be a good bloke.
Please don't hit, and please don't poke.

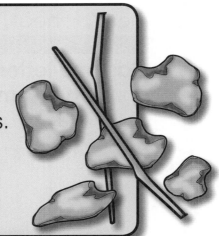

-oke words	*-one* words

Part B:
Let's Play with Words

Divide and Conquer

Directions: Divide each word into parts. Then write the word at the end of the row.

Word	Beginning	Word Family	Word
1. broke	_____	_____	_____
2. stroke	_____	_____	_____
3. stove	_____	_____	_____
4. nose	_____	_____	_____
5. hole	_____	_____	_____
6. whole	_____	_____	_____
7. hope	_____	_____	_____
8. rope	_____	_____	_____

Now write a sentence. Use one or more of the words in the sentence.

_____

_____

Part C:
Let's Read

Poetry Fun

Directions: Read the poem. Circle the *-oa* words. Then draw a picture about the poem.

Float a Row Boat
Based on "Where is Thumbkin?"

Float a row boat,
Float a row boat,
Soaked in foam,
Soaked in foam.
A loaf of bread for brother,
One goat for your mother.
Row them home, row them home.

My Picture

Part D:
Let's Play with Words

Riddle Time

Directions: Write riddles for these words. Then read your riddles to a partner. See if your partner can solve them.

1. road _____

_____

2. toad _____

_____

3. goat _____

_____

Part E:
Let's Grow

Syllable Sort

Directions: Fill in the chart with words from the Word Bank.

Word Bank

soaking	roses	cloakroom	floating	load
throat	croak	coatless	unload	goal
awoke	woven	rope	broke	rode

One syllable (one clap)	Two syllables (two claps)

Part A:
Let's Read

Make Sentences

Directions: Choose the correct word to fill in each blank. Then write sentences for the words at the bottom of the page.

1. (shake, sheep)   We saw _____ at the farm.

2. (rake, rain)   They will _____ up the leaves.

3. (bee, broke)   She got stung by a _____.

4. (rear, right)   Turn _____ at the corner.

5. (bright, bike)   I love to ride my _____.

6. (shade, shame)   It is cool under the tree in

the _____.

7. week   _____

8. brain   _____

Part B:
Let's Play with Words

Word Sort

Directions: Fill in the chart with words from the Word Bank. Write at least one word in each box.

Word Bank

brake	brain	bike	bright	bee	broke	rake
rain	right	sea	roam	pale	pain	pine
peep	poke	shame	shade	sheep	spoke	kite

Ends with silent *e*	Has two vowels together
Has one letter before the word family	**Has two letters before the word family**

Part C:
Let's Read

Divide and Conquer

Directions: Divide each word into parts. Then write the word at the end of the row.

Word	Beginning	Word Family	Ending	Word
1. skate	_____	_____	_____	_____
2. skates	_____	_____	_____	_____
3. pain	_____	_____	_____	_____
4. pains	_____	_____	_____	_____
5. dime	_____	_____	_____	_____
6. dimes	_____	_____	_____	_____
7. light	_____	_____	_____	_____
8. lights	_____	_____	_____	_____

Part D:
Let's Play with Words

Riddle Time

Directions: Choose three words from Unit IV. Write riddles for the words you chose. Read your riddles to a partner. See if your partner can solve them. Then draw a picture for one of the words.

1. _____

_____

2. _____

_____

3. _____

_____

My Picture

Part E:
Let's Grow

Wordo

Directions: This game is like Bingo. Your teacher will give you the words to write in the boxes. Listen to each clue. Use a marker to cover the box for each word you match to the clue. If you get three words in a row, column, or diagonal, call out, "Wordo!"

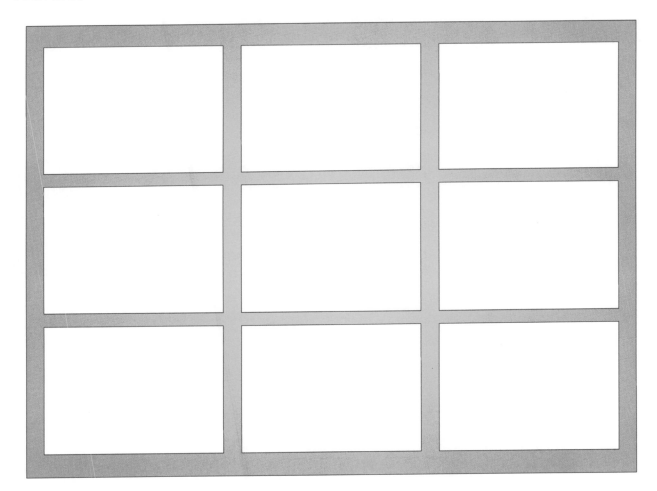

Part A:
Let's Read

Poetry Fun

Directions: Read the poem. Circle the *-er* words. Then fill in the blanks with *-er* words from the Word Bank.

Peter Weeter

Peter Weeter, freeze and fry,
Kissed my sister, made her cry,
Saw my father, Mr. Fister,
Ran away like a twister.

Word Bank

father   Fister   her   Peter   sister   twister   Weeter

_____ _____, freeze and fry,

Kissed my _____, made _____ cry,

Saw my _____, Mr. _____.

Ran away like a _____.

Part B:
Let's Play with Words

Make Sentences

Directions: Complete each sentence with an *-er* word. Then write a sentence using each word you wrote.

1. Someone who teaches is a _____.

_____

_____

2. Someone who plays is a _____.

_____

_____

3. Someone who leads is a _____.

_____

_____

4. Someone who eats is an _____.

_____

_____

Part C:
Let's Read

Poetry Fun

Directions: Read the poem. Circle the *-ar* words. Then answer the questions.

> ## A Smart Little Shark
>
> A smart little shark sat in the dark,
> Preparing for his meal.
> He jumped fast and far,
> But he missed—how bizarre!
> And cried out, "It's hard to catch seal!"

1. How many *-ar* words are in the title? _____

2. How many *-ar* words are in line 1? _____

3. How many *-ar* words are in line 2? _____

4. How many *-ar* words are in line 3? _____

5. How many *-ar* words are in line 4? _____

6. How many *-ar* words are in line 5? _____

7. How many different *-ar* words are in the whole poem? _____

Part D:
Let's Play with Words

Divide and Conquer

Directions: Divide each word into parts. Then write the word at the end of the row.

Word	Beginning	Word Family	Ending	Word
1. scar	_____	_____	_____	_____
2. scars	_____	_____	_____	_____
3. bars	_____	_____	_____	_____
4. car	_____	_____	_____	_____
5. cars	_____	_____	_____	_____
6. far	_____	_____	_____	_____
7. jar	_____	_____	_____	_____
8. jars	_____	_____	_____	_____

Part E:
Let's Grow

Syllable Sort

Directions: Fill in the chart with words from the Word Bank.

Word Bank

government	diaper	flower	scar
summertime	mothering	warning	arm
yardwork	harmful	garden	star

One syllable (one clap)	Two syllables (two claps)	Three syllables (three claps)

Part A:
Let's Read

Poetry Fun

Directions: Read the poems. Circle the -*ook* words. Then answer the questions.

Ring Around the Rookie
Based on "Ring Around the Rosie"
Ring around the rookie,
Read a little booky,
Cookie, Cookie,
We all look down.

Mr. Cook
I know a sad man named Mr. Cook,
Reads all day from his only book.
Took him to the bookstore to take a look.
Found twenty tales, and now he's hooked.

1. How many different -*ook* words are in the poem "Ring Around the Rookie"? _____

2. How many -*ook* words are in the poem "Mr. Cook"? _____

3. Write the line that has more than one -*ook* word.

_____

Part B:
Let's Play with Words

Riddle Time

Directions: Write riddles for these words. Then read your riddles to a partner. See if your partner can solve them.

1. shook   _____

_____

_____

2. book   _____

_____

_____

3. crooked   _____

_____

_____

Poetry Fun

Directions: Read the poem. Circle the -*all* words. Then answer the questions.

Small Baseball
Based on "Row, Row, Row Your Boat"

Small, small, small baseball,
Calling us to play.
Tinier, teenier, tiniest ball,
The pinball rolls away.

Tall, tall, tall football,
Eyeballs stall on you.
Taller and tougher the rugby ball,
They squall and fall on you.

1. Which four –*all* words are compounds? _____

_____ _____ _____

2. How many lines begin with -*all* words? _____

3. How many lines end with -*all* words? _____

Part D:
Let's Play with Words

Write and Draw

Directions: Write sentences for *wall* and *hall*. Then draw a picture of something tall and small.

1. Write a sentence using *wall*.

_____

2. Write a sentence using *hall*.

_____

3. Draw something tall.

4. Draw something small.

Part E:
Let's Grow

Make Words

Directions: Add the beginning sound to the word family. If this makes a real word, write it on the chart.

	-ook	-all
b		
c		
h		
t		

Part A:
Let's Read

Poetry Fun

Directions: Read the poem. Circle the -*ow* words. Then fill in the chart with -*ow* words from the poem.

A Cow

On walks a cow
Who takes a bow,
Then raises its brow
As it hears from the crowd.
A cat cries, "Meow!"
And a dog yells, "Bow wow!"

A few clowny cows
Take final bows,
Which raises some brows
From the loud crowd
Who cry "Meow!"
And "Bow wow wow!"

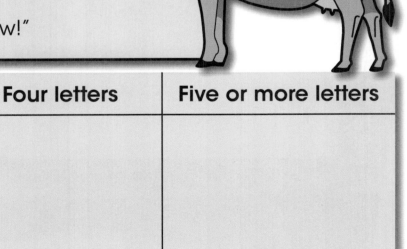

Three letters	Four letters	Five or more letters

Part B:
Let's Play with Words

Divide and Conquer

Directions: Divide each word into parts. Then write the word at the end of the row.

Word	Beginning	Word Family	Ending	Word
1. cow	_____	_____	_____	_____
2. cows	_____	_____	_____	_____
3. bow	_____	_____	_____	_____
4. brow	_____	_____	_____	_____
5. brows	_____	_____	_____	_____
6. how	_____	_____	_____	_____
7. now	_____	_____	_____	_____
8. plows	_____	_____	_____	_____

Part C:
Let's Read

Poetry Fun

Directions: Read the poem. Circle the *-ew* words. Then fill in the blanks in the poem below with words from the Word Bank.

Stew

As the wind whipped and blew,
They brewed a fine stew.
Not a stew for a few,
But for a whole crew.
Soon a crowd grew,
And all enjoyed stew.

Word Bank

blew	crew
few	grew
knew	stew

Stew

As the wind whipped and _____,

They brewed a fine _____.

Not a _____ for a _____,

But for a whole _____.

Soon a crowd _____,

And all enjoyed _____.

Part D:
Let's Play with Words

Riddle Time

Directions: Write riddles for these words. Then read your riddles to a partner. See if your partner can solve them.

1. grew _____

_____

_____

2. flew _____

_____

_____

3. brown _____

_____

_____

Part E:
Let's Grow

Syllable Sort

Directions: Fill in the chart with words from the Word Bank.

Word Bank

newly	grew	new	meow	eyebrow	plowing
cow	viewing	allow	now	chewing	brown

One syllable (one clap)	Two syllables (two claps)

Make Words

Directions: Add the beginning sound to the word family. Choose three words and write a sentence for each.

b, c, h, l, sh	-ook
b, c, f, h, w	-all

b, c, h, n, v	-ow
d, f, n, p, ch	-ew

1. _____

_____

_____

2. _____

_____

_____

3. _____

_____

_____

Part B:
Let's Play with Words

Word Sort

Directions: Fill in the chart with words from the Word Bank.

Word Bank

barn	pinball	flower	chew
book	car	father	now
brook	ball	fever	town
baseball	cookbook	howl	

Has one letter before word family	Has more than one letter before word family
Has one syllable	**Has more than one syllable**

Part C:
Let's Read

Divide and Conquer

Directions: Divide each word into parts. Then write the word at the end of the row.

Word	Beginning	Word Family	Ending	Word
1. books	_____	_____	_____	_____
2. ball	_____	_____	_____	_____
3. cars	_____	_____	_____	_____
4. far	_____	_____	_____	_____
5. her	_____	_____	_____	_____
6. walls	_____	_____	_____	_____
7. jars	_____	_____	_____	_____
8. stars	_____	_____	_____	_____

Part D:
Let's Play with Words

Riddle Time

Directions: Choose three words from Unit V. Write riddles for these words. Read your riddles to a partner. See if your partner can solve them. Then draw a picture for one of the words.

1. _____

_____

2. _____

_____

3. _____

_____

My Picture